THE CALM
COLOURING BOOK

THE CALM
COLOURING BOOK
Beautiful images to soothe your cares away

ARCTURUS

This edition published in 2015 by Arcturus Publishing Limited
26/27 Bickels Yard, 151–153 Bermondsey Street,
London SE1 3HA

ISBN: 978-1-78404-631-6
AD004596NT

Printed in Spain

Introduction

It's official – colouring is good for you! Whatever your age, shading a picture in colours of your choice generates a sense of stillness and wellness. It also stimulates brain areas related to motor skills and creativity. Colouring works as a relaxation technique – calming the mind and occupying the hands – and helps you enter a freer state of being.

The Calm Colouring Book contains gorgeous images of birds, leaves, flowers, fish, butterflies and tranquil landscapes to soothe the mind and please the senses. By colouring in the outlines you will de-stress your mind and body and create your own beautiful artworks. So put your worries on hold, pick up your crayons, pencils or felt-tips, and get ready to unleash your creative side…

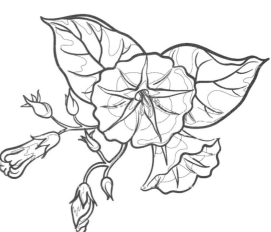

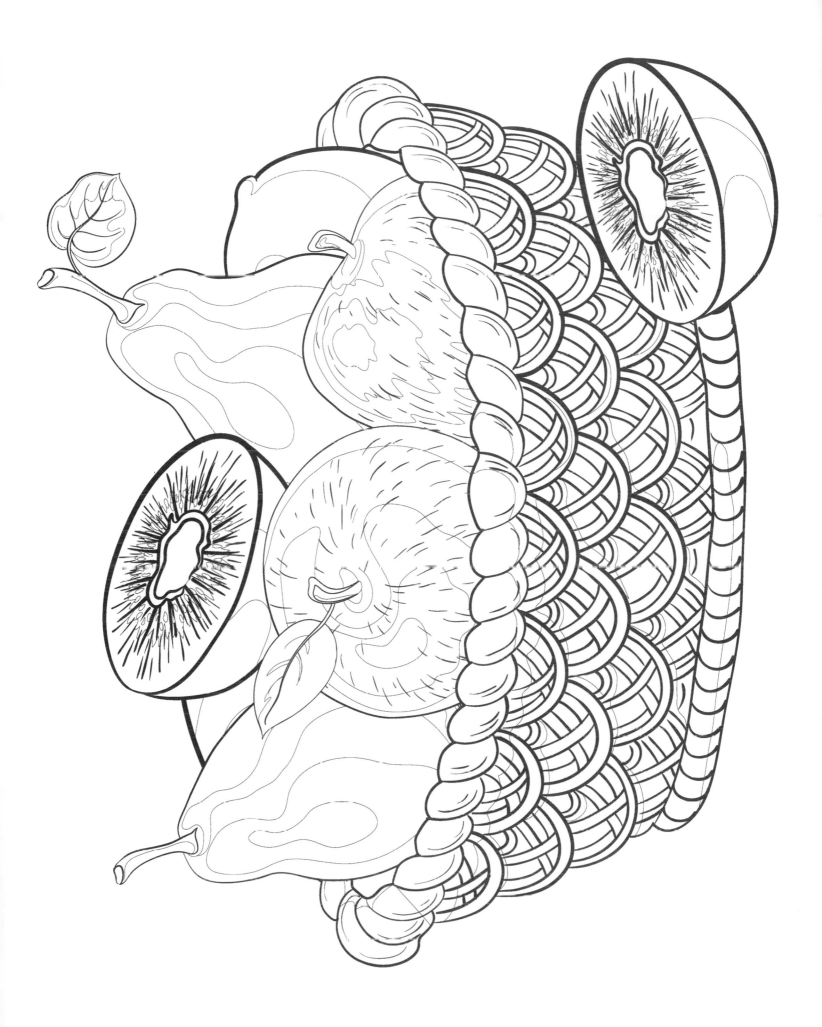

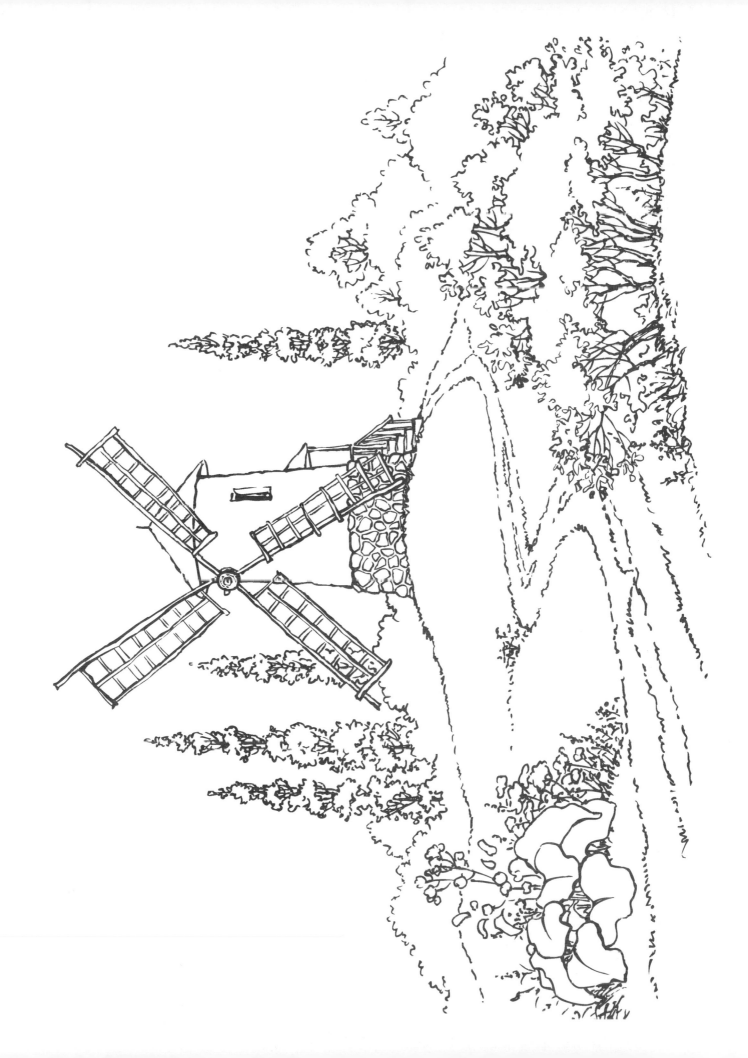

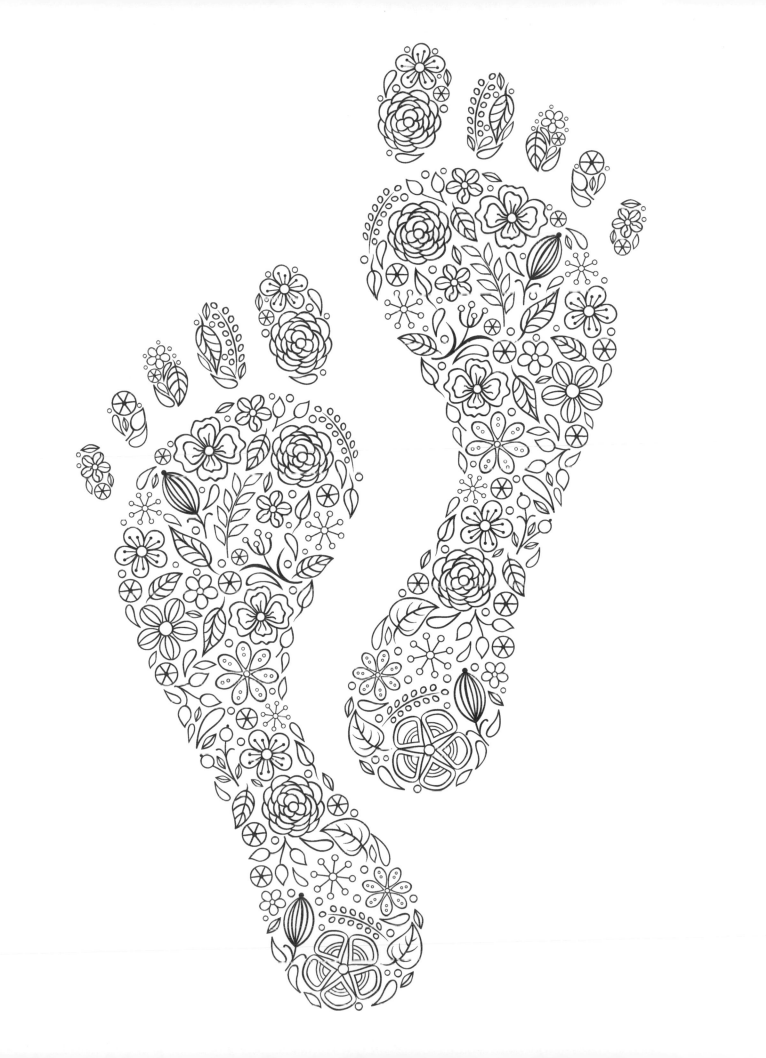

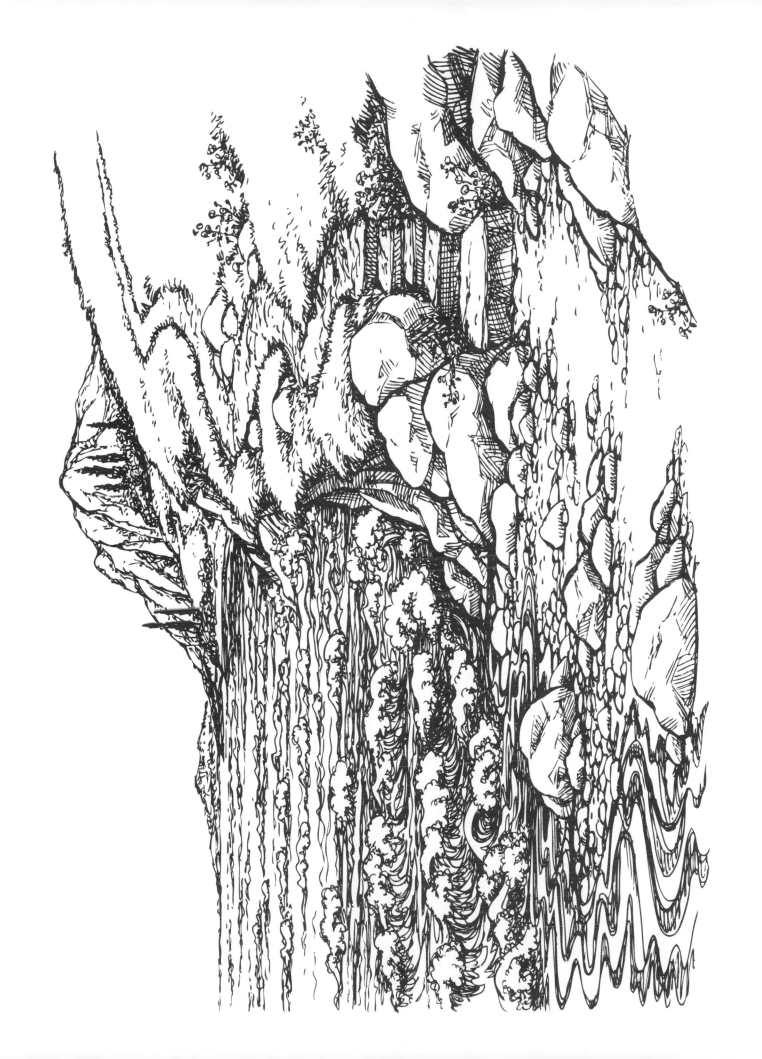

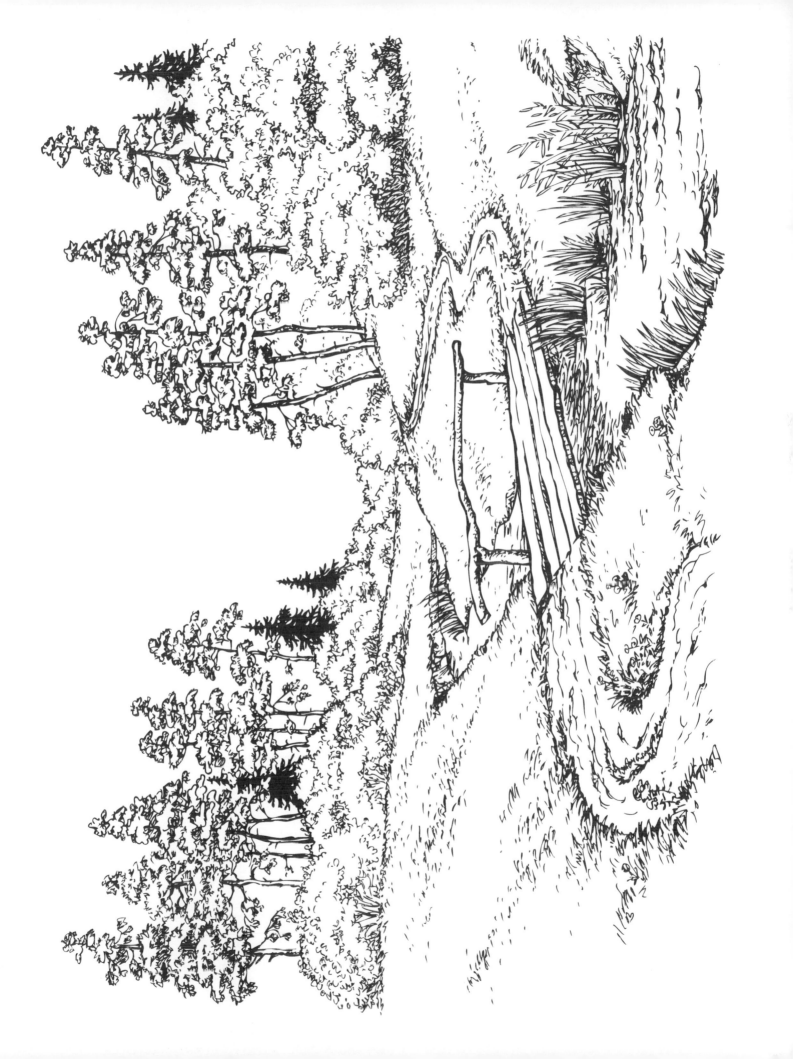